THE KRYPTON FACTOR QUIZ BOOK

D1638662

BASED ON THE GRANADA TELEVISION SERIES

B■XTREE

First published in Great Britain in 1989 by Boxtree Ltd.

Text © David Elias, Geoff Kershaw, Peter Taylor,
   Gerry Wickham 1989
Krypton Factor © Granada Television 1989
Copyright in this compilation © Boxtree Limited 1989

Designed and typeset by ML Design, London.
Printed and bound in Great Britain by
Cox & Wyman Ltd, Reading, Berkshire

9 8 7 6 5 4 3

For Boxtree Limited
2nd Floor
Broadwall House
21 Broadwall
London
SE1 9PL

Front cover design: Head Productions

British Library Cataloguing in Publication Data
The krypton factor quiz book.
   1. General knowledge. Questions & answers
   793.73

   ISBN 1–85283–266–5

CONTENTS

CONTENTS

INTRODUCTION

The Krypton Factor, aptly described as British television's toughest quiz, was launched by Granada in 1977. It differs from other quiz shows in several respects. It offers no cash prizes, gifts or free holidays – and there is only one winner. Out of 36 contestants each year, who have been selected from thousands of applicants, one person will emerge to gain the coveted title of United Kingdom Superperson.

For the past 12 years the quiz has been presented by Gordon Burns, who writes the programme scripts and helps to devise some of the tests. He enjoyed a long career on television as interviewer, documentary producer and writer before turning freelance; he currently presents the successful Searchline feature in *Surprise, Surprise* and the word-association quiz *Password*.

The Krypton Factor, relayed in 13 weekly programmes from September to November, comprises six tests on Mental Agility, Response, Observation, Intelligence, Physical Ability and General Knowledge. This book focuses on four of those subjects, although the tests on the printed page necessarily differ slightly from those seen on television. Every page is devoted to a particular area or skill and is easily identified by the logo at the top of the page.

= Intelligence   = Mental Agility

= General Knowledge   = Physical Ability

Most of the questions have been used for testing qualifiers; so when you attempt them you will be pitting your wits, your ability, your knowledge and your physical stamina against the actual contestants. The various mental disciplines require, more than anything else,

patience and common sense. The Physical Ability tests are designed to measure and promote fitness, not to push you to impossible limits. If you are in any doubt as to whether they are for you, seek medical advice first.

Remember that, unlike the contestants, who are working against the clock, in most of these tests you have no time limits. So you really can treat them as fun. After all, there can only be one winner – you!

Notes on Contributors

David Elias is a professional question setter. He competed in the 1980 series of *The Krypton Factor*, and even though he was disqualified for missing out the water jump on the assault course in his heat, reached the final and finished third. He has contributed to numerous TV quizzes, most of which are still being shown. His broad advice for improving your general knowledge is to take an interest in what's happening in the world.

Geoff Kershaw spent many years in the hotel business and, with his wife Cheryl, now concentrates on producing quizzes for TV and company conferences, working from his home in the Lake District. He reached the semi-finals of *The Krypton Factor* in 1981 and has worked on the series ever since.

Dr Peter Taylor is a clinical psychologist, whose help was invited during the planning stages of *The Krypton Factor*. Since then he has regularly submitted ideas and tests for the series. His general advice for the puzzles is to decide first on your strategy, do something else for a while if you get stuck, and keep a cool head.

Dr Gerald Wickham, a mathematics lecturer at the University of Manchester, has been devising intelligence-testing puzzles and games for *The Krypton Factor* from its very start, more than 200 programmes in all. He has also contributed to a number of other TV quizzes.

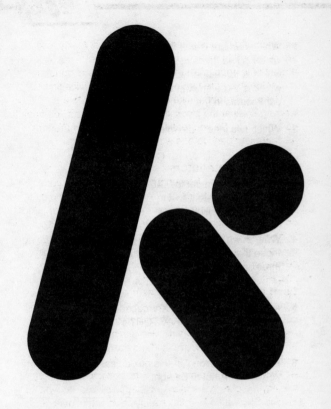

QUESTIONS

1. Which number is half the number,
   which is two thirds of the number,
   which is three quarters of the number,
   which is three times the number of
   contestants in the Krypton Final?

2. Which two letters are missing from this set?

   U N __ C __ F

3. If – 40 is equivalent to – 40
   And 5 is equivalent to 41
   What is 20 equivalent to?

4. Write down the numbers from one to twenty excluding
   those that are not even or that are not divisible by
   three or four.

5. If XIXVIIIIXXVXVIXXXVXIV decodes as KRYPTON,
   What is the code for FACTOR?

6. Do not write 'wrong' in this box unless you don't want
   your answer not to be right.

7. Steve didn't not beat Gerry to buy the first round of
   drinks. Geoff couldn't not avoid not buying the round
   after Pete. Gordon neither didn't not buy the drinks
   before Gerry nor wasn't not able to buy them after
   Pete.

   Who bought the third round of drinks?

Answers on page 78

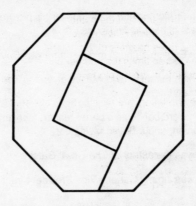

The octagon drawn above is made up of three shapes. If two of them are cut in *half* the resulting five shapes can be used to fill completely the square below.

Where are the cuts to be made, and how do you fill the square?

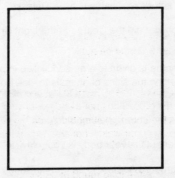

Answers on page 78

GENERAL KNOWLEDGE 1

1. Which French painter is famous for his pictures of the dancers of the Moulin Rouge?

2. Which English author's middle name was Boynton?

3. On which mountain was Moses given the Ten Commandments?

4. Which word connects a barrel-maker, a boxing champion, and a British racing car?

5. Who was the author of *The Great Gatsby*?

6. Who was Jimmy Carter's Vice-President from 1976 to 1980?

7. Which chemical element was once known as brimstone?

8. To which larger island does Gozo belong?

9. Which King was the husband of Marie Antoinette?

10. Which actor's real name is Issur Demsky?

11. In which war did the Charge of the Light Brigade occur?

12. What name is given to a person skilled in preparing and stuffing the skins of animals to look like live animals?

13. What is the chemical symbol for iron?

14. Whereabouts in your body is your clavicle?

15. If you ordered *homard grillé* from a French menu, what would you expect to get?

Answers on page 78

1. If 8, 2, 10, 3 means TONE
    What do 1, 7, 8, 9, 4 mean?

2. If 7, 18, 13, 2 means TINY
    What do 19, 6, 20, 22 mean?

3. If 1, 23, 31, 15, 1, 3, 9, 39 means ALPHABET
    What does 1, 27, 37, 45, 9, 35 mean?

4. If 3, 11, 9, 12, 6 means TENTS
    What does 16, 2, 1, 19, 18, 16 mean?

5. If 10, 28, 18, 14, 26, 2 means ENIGMA
    What does 32, 2, 36, 2, 8, 30, 48 mean?

6. If 8, 3, 2, 9 means HEWN
    What does 5, 6, 1, 7 mean?

7. If 5, 20, 110, 25, 90, 10 means ADVERB
    What does 80, 90, 75, 70, 75, 105, 70 mean?

8. If D, G, B, K, M, D, O, F, F means CHALLENGE
    What does W, H, D, S, P, Q, Z mean?

Answers on page 79

1. What does a cartographer draw?
2. Maputo is the capital of which country run by Frelimo, between Zimbabwe and the Indian Ocean?
3. For which 1984 film about Mozart did F. Murray Abraham win an Oscar?
4. Which artist whose first name was Amadeo was famous for painting women with elongated faces?
5. Which medal are American servicemen awarded when wounded in action?
6. Purple Emperor, Monarch and Grayling are varieties of what?
7. In which English county are Buttermere, Bassenthwaite and Derwent Water?
8. 'Cumberland Gap' and 'Gamblin' Man' were number one hits for which singer of skiffle in 1957?
9. The dong is the unit of currency of which Asian country whose capital is Hanoi?
10. What do the letters VTOL stand for in aircraft designations?
11. Verdigris is a green layer that forms on which metal exposed to moist air?
12. Sir John Hermon has been Chief Constable since 1980 of which force often called simply the RUC?
13. Ulster, Inverness, Chesterfield and Burberry are all what sort of garment?
14. Which resort on the Côte d'Azur holds an annual film festival that awards the Golden Palm?
15. Who wrote _Cannery Row_, _The Grapes of Wrath_ and _Of Mice and Men_?
16. What sort of animals are steinboks, elands, kudus and klipspringers?
17. Which surgeon sailed on the 'Antelope' and was shipwrecked on Lilliput, according to Jonathan Swift?

Answers on page 79

1	3
2	4

IS TO

3	4
6	7

AND

9	7
4	8

IS TO

13	16
12	15

AS

V	VI
IX	X

IS TO

(COMPLETE
THE BLANKS)

Answers on page 79

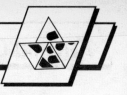

This diagram shows the 19 moons of the planet Krypton. By numbering them in itinerary order, plan a trip which visits each planet once only, returning to base on planet Krypton. For the sake of fuel economy and space traffic control, you must not retrace any part of your path and you must use the spaceways provided.

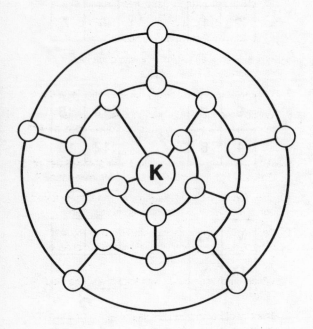

Answers on page 80

GENERAL KNOWLEDGE 2

1. Which chemical element has the symbol K?

2. In which town are the headquarters of the Open University?

3. On board which ship did Sir Joseph Porter take his sisters and his cousins and his aunts?

4. Which animals are all descended from a single litter found in Aleppo, Syria, in 1930?

5. Who was the first woman in space?

6. Which European capital city was once called Christiania?

7. Which word means literally 'Lasting only for a day'?

8. Which novel begins, 'It was the best of times, it was the worst of times, it was the age of wisdom, it was the age of foolishness'?

9. With whom do you associate 'Piper at the Gates of Dawn', 'Saucerful of Secrets' and 'Ummagumma'?

10. Of which building did the Elgin Marbles (now found in London's British Museum) once form a part?

11. Which prison reformer became in 1818 the first woman ever to give evidence before a House of Commons Committee?

12. Which Italian composer was known as 'The Red Priest'?

13. The city of Leningrad took its present name in 1924, when it was changed from what?

14. Whose last voyage was to the Houyhnhnms?

15. What is the principal vegetable ingredient of moussaka?

Answers on page 80

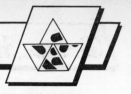

The contented cat may be packed into the accompanying square. Show how by marking the square with straight lines and labelling the corresponding subdivisions with the corresponding parts of the 'Krypton Kat'.

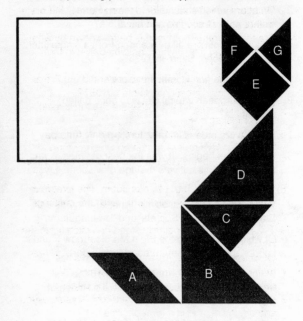

Answer on page 80

Important Before answering the questions below, read the notes on page 12.

1. What's the Roman numeral for one thousand?
2. What does the 'M' stand for in the name of E.M.Forster, author of '*A Room With a View*'?
3. Francis Morgan Thompson is better known by what name as a double Olympic gold medallist in the decathlon?
4. About which tabloid daily newspaper did the Press Council uphold most complaints in 1987?
5. Khawarij, Sunni and what else are the three main sects of Islam?
6. The novels *She*, *Allan Quartermain* and *King Solomon's Mines* were written by which author?
7. Where can you find Haggai, Joel, Esther, Malachi and Numbers?
8. Who set to music the religious poem 'The Dream of Gerontius', and wrote the 'Pomp and Circumstance' marches?
9. The Elgin Marbles originally stood on which hill in the city of Athens?
10. Of which country has Accra been capital since 1957?
11. In the 1970s, James Garner played which TV detective who lived in a caravan at the beach?
12. Which mineral has varieties called rock crystal, citrine and amethyst, and is a form of silica?
13. How many quarts make two and a half gallons?
14. Which horse, the ten-length winner of the 1981 Derby, was later kidnapped from a stud in Ireland?
15. Who wrote *Shirley*, *The Professor* and *Jane Eyre*?
16. In which event did athlete Charlie Spedding win a bronze medal in the 1984 Olympics, behind Carlos Lopez?

Answers on page 81

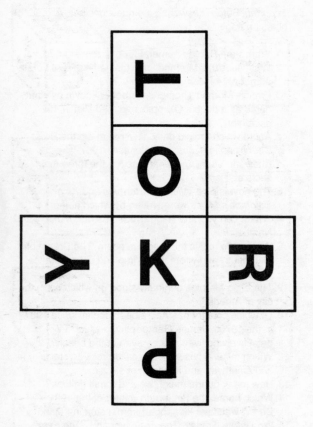

Which of the eight dice on the following page could not have been made from the plan above?

Answer on page 81

1

2

3

4

5

6

7

8

In the figure drawn below six straight lines enclose eight equilateral triangles of three different sizes. Can you find a completely different and simpler way of drawing six straight lines which enclose eight such triangles of just two different sizes.

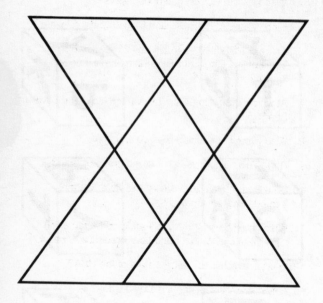

Answer on page 81

GENERAL KNOWLEDGE 3

1. Who designed the first British jet aircraft?

2. Which West Indies fast bowler is known to other cricketers as 'Whispering Death'?

3. 1682, 1758, 1834, 1910 and 1986 – with which traveller do you connect these dates?

4. Who was the Roman god of doorways?

5. King, Magellan, Jackass and Chinstrap are all what?

6. There is a South African city called Kaapstad by some of its inhabitants. By what name is it better known?

7. At which international film festival are Gold and Silver Bears given as prizes?

8. Who wrote the novels *Pale Fire* and *Lolita*?

9. Road Town is the capital of which group of islands?

10. Mike Rutherford, Tony Banks and Peter Gabriel formed which rock group?

11. Which member of the Royal Family is the father of Lady Gabriella Windsor and Lord Frederick Windsor?

12. In area, which is the largest state of the USA?

13. Which singer's real name is David Cook?

14. What is a *Vulpes vulpes*?

15. Which country has a name meaning 'The Saviour' in English?

Answers on page 81

ODD ONE OUT

1. Which of these words is the odd one out?

   FILM   HOST   BENT   ARCH   FLUX   BLOW

2. Which of these letters is the odd one out?

   A   H   T   I   O   M

3. Which of these letters is the odd one out?

   R   A   Y   G   B   I   V

4. Which of these letters are the odd ones out?

   N   C   R   P   O   T   Q   Y   K

SPATIAL LOGIC 5

The four gears drawn below have 45, 25, 10 and 5 teeth respectively. An arrow is marked on each gear, and initially, each arrow points up. How many revolutions must the smallest gear perform before all the arrows point up again?

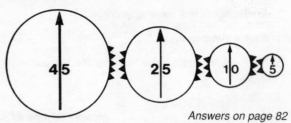

Answers on page 82

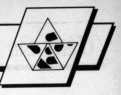

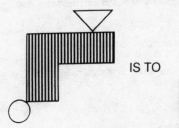

IS TO

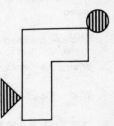

AS

IS TO **?**

Answer on page 82.

1. What is the former country of Northern Rhodesia now called?

2. Chukkas are used in which sport?

3. What's the common name for acetylsalicylic acid?

4. Who is the Poet Laureate?

5. How much is a 'monkey'?

6. To which country do the Canary Islands belong?

7. How many points does a touchdown score in American football?

8. Who wrote the novel *The Good Terrorist*?

9. What term is used for a victory which costs more in casualties than the triumph was worth?

10. Who was killed by Sirhan Sirhan?

11. What do 100 kopeks make?

12. Whose picture appears on the reverse side of a £50 note?

13. With which sport do you associate Hartwig Steenken?

14. Which poet's first names were Dante Gabriel?

15. In which month is St Swithin's day?

Answers on page 82

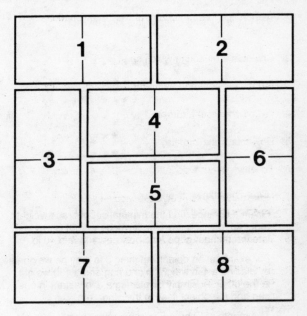

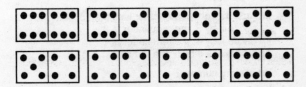

Arranging the dominoes in the eight positions shown, how many rows can you get to add up to 19?

Answer on page 83

MATHEMATICAL MUDDLES

1. Fill in the missing digits in this long division.

```
              * * *
        _____
* * * / * * * * * *
        * 0 * *
        * * * *
        * 5 0 *
          * * *
          * 4 *
```

Clue The answer is unique!

2. Given a balance, find the minimal set of brass weights required to weigh any object whose weight is any integral number of pounds between 1 lb and 40 lb.

   For example, an object weighing 3 lb may be weighed by placing a 4 lb weight in one pan and a 1 lb weight in the other, or simply by placing a 3 lb weight in one pan and the object itself in the other, etc.

3. The month of February in every year exactly divisible by four has 29 days; how many months in these years have 30 days?

4. I've just thought of a number less than 60.
   If I divide it by 3, the remainder is 2.
   If I divide it by 4, the remainder is 1.
   And if I divide it by 5, the remainder is 4.

   What's my number?

5. *The story of a former bank cashier*

   A man goes into a bank to cash a cheque. The cashier inadvertently misreads the cheque and gives the man the same number of pounds as there were pence written on the cheque and the same number of

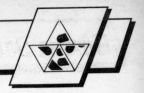

pence as there were pounds. The man then leaves the bank and calls at a newsagent where he purchases a box of matches for 5p. On counting his money, he then finds that he has exactly twice the amount written on the cheque.

What was the correct value of the cheque?

6. At a christening party, including the baby being christened, the guests consisted of the following: 6 mothers, 4 fathers, 1 grandfather, 3 grandmothers, 1 great-grandmother, 7 brothers, 3 sisters, 7 cousins, 4 aunties, 3 uncles, 2 nieces, 5 nephews, 2 brothers-in-law and 4 sisters-in-law.

What is the minimum number of guests possible who went to the party?

7. A man goes to a tub of water with two empty jars. Jar A holds exactly 3 pints and jar B 5 pints. Using only the jars and the water, how can he bring back exactly 4 pints of water?

8. One glass is half full of Claret, the other is half full of water. From the first glass a teaspoonful of wine is taken out and poured into the glass containing water. A teaspoonful of the mixture in the second is then transferred to the first glass. Is the quantity of Claret removed from the first glass greater or less than the quantity of water removed from the second glass?

9. A millionaire was in love with a beautiful woman. On New Year's Day he gave her a present. On 2 January he gave her two presents and on the 3 January, three presents, and so on until on 31 December he gave her 365 presents. She decided to marry him to stop the presents coming. How many presents had she received in that year?

10. How many times can 4 be subtracted from 98?

Answers on page 83

Important Before answering the questions below, read the notes on page 12.

1. Mathematically, a straight line from a circle's centre to its circumference is called what?

2. Which bone lies alongside the radius in the human forearm?

3. Vladimir Ilich Ulyanov, born in Simbirsk in 1870, was better known by what name?

4. Which actor married Rula Lenska in 1987?

5. Which stretch of water is known to the French as *La Manche*?

6. In 1875, who became the first man to swim the English Channel?

7. In which musical by Webber & Stilgoe do the cast use roller skates to portray railway trains?

8. What breed was Starlite Express, the Cruft's supreme champion of 1988?

9. Which city was the setting for the film *Letter to Brezhnev*?

10. To which Liverpool group did the singer Holly Johnson belong?

11. The French franc is divided into a hundred what?

12. 91.44 centimetres is equivalent to which imperial measure?

13. 'Yardbird', or 'Bird', was the nickname of which jazz saxophonist?

14. Who wrote *Mansfield Park* and *Northanger Abbey*?

15. Austin is the capital of which state of the USA, called the Lone Star State?

16. Which tax, called CTT for short, was replaced by Inheritance Tax in 1986?

17. What's the capital of Chile?

Answers on page 84

1. If you have two coins of the realm in your pocket worth 11p and one of them is not a 10 pence piece, what are they?

2. What's next in this sequence?

   I   VIII   III   X   V

3. If $A^2E^1U^3A^1O^4E^1$ spells BEWARE
   What does $O^5A^3O^4A^1O^2E^1$ spell?

4. Every alternate century starts out on the same day of the week – which one?

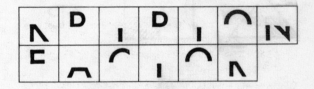

5. Complete the well-known phrase above.

6. *A Captain's problem!*
   A ship carrying, as passengers, 15 baddies and 15 goodies, encountered a storm and in order to save the ship and the crew, one-half of the passengers had to be thrown into the sea. Accordingly, the passengers were placed in a circle and every ninth man, reckoning from a certain point, was cast overboard. The Captain of the ship, in his relentless pursuit of truth, justice and the American way of life, had found an arrangement by which all the goodies would be saved. Can you find such an arrangement?

Answers on page 84

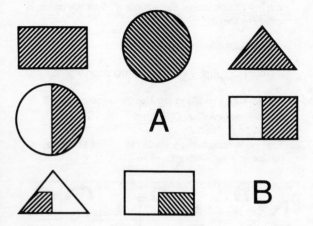

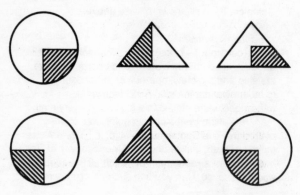

Which of the following fit gaps A and B.

Answer on page 84

1. Which film star married Joanne Woodward in 1955?

2. What's the capital of Turkey?

3. What's the study of poisons called?

4. Mount Usborne is the highest mountain where?

5. Who was 'The Man With The Golden Trumpet'?

6. Who said 'Religion is the opium of the people'?

7. Farsi is which country's official language?

8. Who wrote *Goodbye Mr Chips*?

9. Which chemical element's name means 'hidden' in Greek?

10. Which singer named his 1986 album after Elvis Presley's home?

11. The Sabin vaccine protects against what?

12. In a restaurant, 'lyonnaise' means which vegetable is used?

13. Under what name did Lynn Stringer become known in show business?

14. Which King of England was called 'Lackland'?

15. Mrs Gro Harlem Bruntland holds what position in politics?

Answers on page 85

Important Before answering the questions below, read the notes on page 12.

1. What is waved to indicate the finish of a Grand Prix in motor racing?
2. The flag of which EEC country has three horizontal bands of red, yellow and red, with a coat of arms in the centre?
3. Which King of Spain married Queen Mary I of England in 1554?
4. Phillumenists collect which articles used by smokers and others?
5. In a boxing match, how long does each round last?
6. Which highwayman is the central character of *The Threepenny Opera* and of *The Beggar's Opera* ?
7. From whom did Edward Heath take over as leader of the Conservative Party?
8. The vitreous humour is inside which organ of the body?
9. What did the initials I. K. stand for in the name of the great engineer I. K. Brunel?
10. Which country is called the Hashemite Kingdom, and has Amman as its capital?
11. The River Jordan flows finally into which sea?
12. Which actor who died in 1988 was married to Helen Cherry, and starred in the film *Brief Encounter* ?
13. Which cabinet office did Sir Geoffrey Howe hold before becoming Foreign Secretary in 1983?
14. In which sport may an opponent be held in chancery, a Boston Crab or a Flying Mare?
15. Restormel, Caradon and Penwith are District Councils of which English county?
16. In which play does the Duke of Cornwall marry Regan, sister of Goneril and Cordelia?
17. Besides Italy, the lira is the currency of which country partly in Europe and partly in Asia, whose capital is Ankara?

Answers on page 85

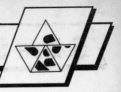

IS TO

AS

IS TO

?

Answer on page 85

IF

AND

WHAT DOES

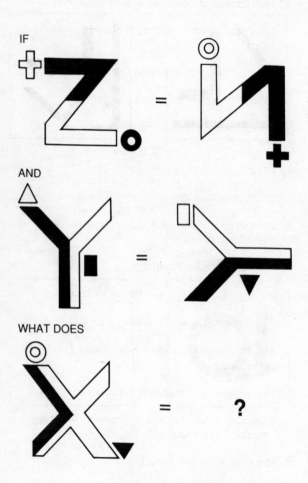

= ?

Answer on page 86

1. Who composed the music for 'West Side Story'?

2. What's the treatment and study of skin diseases called?

3. What is the largest lake in the British Isles?

4. Which Island calls itself 'Ellan Vannin'?

5. If nectar was the drink of the Greek gods, what was their food?

6. Which fruit is *fraise* in French?

7. Which poet fell in love with Fanny Brawne?

8. What name is given to a line on a map which joins places of equal height?

9. What is the capital of California?

10. What was Britain's longest-running TV quiz?

11. Who wrote the novel *The Radiant Way* ?

12. Which film actor's real name was Emmanuel Goldenberg?

13. Which English city has two 20th century cathedrals?

14. 'A Scandal in Bohemia' was the first story about which famous fictional character?

15. Who directed the film *Birdy* ?

Answers on page 86

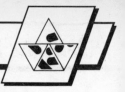

What is the next shape *but one* in the following sequence?

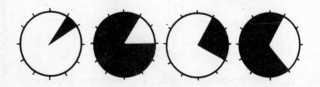

Your answer should be one of the following:

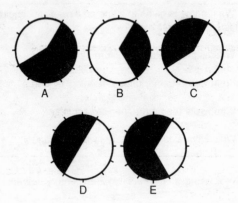

Answer on page 86

NUMBER GRID

1	5	8	3
9	13	15	6
7	16	10	11
4	14	12	2

Which number is positioned below the number, which is twice the number, that's twice the number, that's a third of the number, to the left of the number below 11?

LOGIC GRID

- Alfred scored more than the redhead but less than the doctor.
- Bill scored less than the blonde.
- Charles scored more than the brunette.
- The sailor scored less than the actor.

Using this information, fill in the grid below.

	Name	Hair Colour	Occupation
Highest Score			
Middle Score			
Lowest Score			

Answers on page 87

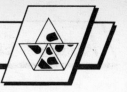

The diagram on the left contains all the logical clues to colour the figure on the right.

Do this using the code

R = red   O = orange   G = green
Y = yellow   B = blue

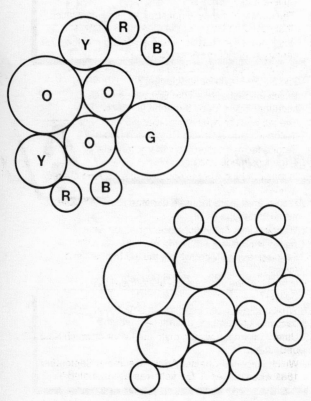

Answer on page 87

BUZZER SEQUENCE 5

Important Before answering the questions below, read the notes on page 12.

1. To which country do the Dodecanese and Ionian islands belong?
2. Which actress became in 1981 the Greek Minister of Culture and Science?
3. 'The quality of mercy is not strained' is said in which Shakespeare play by Portia, posing as a lawyer?
4. Which Venetian traveller wrote an account in the 13th century of his journeys to Mongolia?
5. In which book by Mark Twain do Huckleberry Finn and Becky Thatcher first appear?
6. Which union that has Tom Sawyer as general secretary is known by the abbreviation NUPE?
7. The job of a cordwainer involved working with which material associated with Cordoba in Spain?
8. Before decimalisation, how many 'tanners' or sixpences made one pound?
9. In music, which word is opposite of *forte*, and means quietly?
10. Pianist Ignace Paderewski became Prime Minister of which country in 1919?
11. Who was the Polish-born director of the films *Rosemary's Baby* and *Tess* ?
12. To the nearest metre, what's the world pole vault record?
13. In which of the six counties of Northern Ireland is Belfast?
14. What name is often used for an antirrhinum flower because it resembles a creature's mouth?
15. Uther Pendragon was in myth the father of which King of Britain?
16. Which office did Chester Arthur assume in September 1881 when James A. Garfield was assassinated?

Answers on page 87

LOGIC PUZZLES 3

1. In the century and a half between 1725 and 1875 the French fought and won a certain battle on the 22nd April of one year and 4382 days later, also on the 22nd April, they gained·another victory. The sum of the digits of these two victorious years is 40.

   When were the battles?

2. If you had only one match, and entered a cold room where there was an oil lamp, oil heater and some kindling wood, which would you light first?

3. How many of each animal did Moses take aboard the ark?

4. Complete this sound series:

   98.4   88.5   90.2   ____

5. Which letters are next in this sequence:

   Y T I L I G A L A T N __ __

6. In a street of eight houses four on each side, you live opposite the house worth £30,000 which is two to the right of the house opposite the house valued at £15,000 which is three to the left of the house on the right of the house worth £20,000.

   How much is your house worth?.

7. Fifteen people ran the assault course. All but seven finished the course dry. How many fell in the water?

Answers on page 88

The diagram shows a typical street with the number of the house, the name of the occupant, and the colour of the front door clearly printed on each house front. The relationship of one house to another is determined from the front of the house looking towards the centre of the road. Thus house No.5 is to the left of house No.3, whilst house No.2 is to the right of house No.6. Bearing this in mind, study the details on the illustration below for 60 seconds. Then turn the page and try to answer as many questions as you can.

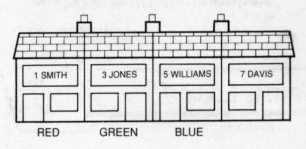

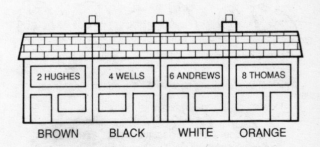

1. What is the number of the house one to the left of the house opposite Mr Wells' house?

2. What is the colour of the front door opposite the house two to the right of house No.2?

3. Who lives in the house two to the left of the house opposite the house one to the left of the house with the white front door?

4. What colour is the door of the house one to the left of the house opposite the house two to the right of the house opposite the house to the right of Mr Jones' house?

Answers on page 88

SPATIAL LOGIC 13

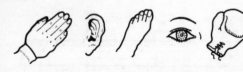

Which of the following completes the above sequence?

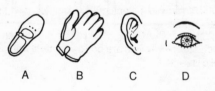

A   B   C   D

Answer on page 88

1. Which metal is obtained from the ore galena?

2. Who draws 'Doonesbury'?

3. Tripoli is the capital of which country?

4. In which film did Kirk Douglas play Vincent Van Gogh?

5. Who was the first singer to have a number one hit with 'Green Door'?

6. Which heroine saved nine people from a shipwreck in 1838 off Northumbria?

7. Which painter married his model Rosella Segreto in 1976?

8. Which creatures sang 'We All Stand Together' in a cartoon film?

9. With which athletics event do you associate Javier Sotomayor?

10. In Shakespeare, who kills Desdemona?

11. What's the family home of the Duke of Marlborough?

12. Jean-Claude Duvalier used to rule which country?

13. Who painted 'The Night Watch'?

14. In which city was a stadium built, but not used, for the 1936 Olympics?

15. Which author's novels are borrowed most from British public libraries?

Answers on page 88

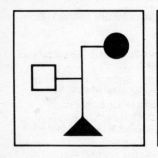

IS TO

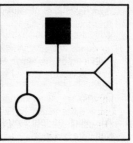

AS

IS TO

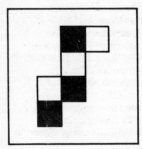

Answer on page 88

Important Before answering the questions below, please read the notes on page 12.

1. The rivers Witham, Welland, Nene and Ouse flow into which inlet of the North Sea?
2. Which volcano in Washington State erupted in May 1980?
3. In mythology, who kidnapped Helen from her husband Menelaus, and took her back to Troy?
4. In Paris, it's called the *Boulévard Périphérique* – what's such a road called in English?
5. The book *Ring of Bright Water* is about Gavin Maxwell's experiences with which animals?
6. Which poet born in Ottery St Mary in Devon wrote 'Cristabel', 'Kubla Khan' and 'The Ancient Mariner'?
7. A Rhodesian ridgeback is a breed of which creature?
8. Which singer's hits include 'Hounds of Love', 'Wow' and 'Wuthering Heights'?
9. Bushido is the traditional code of which warrior class who rose to power in Japan?
10. In modern warfare, SAM is short for what kind of weapon?
11. Which aviation pioneer, 100 years old in January 1988, made planes called the Camel and the Pup?
12. Which Greek soprano, prima donna of La Scala, Milan, in the 1950s, was a close friend of Aristotle Onassis?
13. The drink Calvados is made from which fruit?
14. The Appleton layer or F-layer in the upper atmosphere reflects which waves?
15. Which broadcaster who married the dancer Moira Shearer in 1950 presented TVs *Did You See*?
16. Which musical instrument do Nigel Kennedy, Stephan Grappelli and Yehudi Menuhin play?
17. The violent 1979 film *Mad Max* was made in which country?

Answers on page 89

1. Which of the following is the odd one out?

   EYE   PEG   TEA   SEA   WHY   ARE

2. The Pilot and the Cook are lawfully married but the Cook is not the Pilot's legal wife.

   Explain.

3. Explain this sequence:

   ABCDEFGHJKLMNPRSTVWXYABCDEFG

4. What is the missing number in this sequence:

   100   200   400   800   ?   5,000   10,000

5. In a row of five houses Dave lives next door to the football player and two doors away from Jane the windsurfer. The squash player lives next door to Sue whilst the windsurfer lives next door to Harry and four doors away from John whose house is next door to the tennis player who lives two doors away from the footballer. Harry lives next door to the golfer.

   Which game does Dave play?

6. What is $\frac{1}{3}$ of $\frac{1}{2}$ of the sum of two numbers for one of which $\frac{1}{4}$ of $\frac{1}{4}$ is $\frac{1}{4}$ and for the other $\frac{1}{2}$ of $\frac{1}{2}$ is $\frac{1}{2}$?

Answers on page 89

Below are two views of the same dice. Using this information complete the plan below. Make sure the dots are put in the correct places!

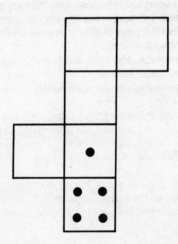

Answer on page 89

Important Before answering the questions below, read the notes on page 12.

1. Which unit of British currency ceased to be legal tender on 11 March, 1988?
2. In which system of weights did the pound contain twelve ounces, each of twenty pennyweight?
3. Who wrote the poem 'Troilus & Criseyde' in the 1380s, after 'The Book of the Duchess'?
4. The Archbishop of Canterbury's London home is which palace?
5. In the borough of Lambeth, the Cottesloe and the Lyttleton are part of which arts complex?
6. In an operating theatre, nitrous oxide may be used for what purpose?
7. Who slept for twenty years in the Catskill Mountains, in a story written by Washington Irving?
8. In which sport have Hans Winkler, Gerhard Wiltfang and Gail Greenhough been World Champions?
9. Who wrote the plays *Equus*, *Amadeus* and *The Royal Hunt of the Sun*?
10. The Shaftesbury Memorial in Piccadilly Circus is popularly known as what?
11. What nationality was the great scholar Erasmus, who died in 1536?
12. What is the Dutch language of Belgium called?
13. Fleming, Florey and Chain shared the 1945 Nobel Prize for Medicine for their work on which antibiotic?
14. Which Pennsylvanian city's name means 'Brotherly Love'?
15. Philip Pirrip is the central character of which novel?
16. Who ordered the signal 'England expects that everyone will do his duty' to be flown before his last battle in 1805?

Answers on page 90

IF   BECOMES

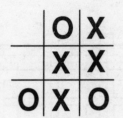   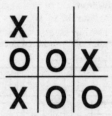

WHAT DOES   BECOME?

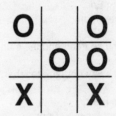   

Fill in the empty grid above.

Answer on page 90

A row of five terraced houses are occupied by five men with different jobs from different counties. Using the clues given below, work out who does what and where they come from.

- The joiner lives on the end, next to the man from Lincolnshire.
- Sid lives two doors away from Eric.
- Frank lives next door to the seaman.
- Claud lives in No 5.
- The teacher lives between the seaman and the man from Devon.
- The plumber lives two doors away from the teacher.
- Claud is a seaman.
- Bert's neighbour comes from Kent.
- Eric lives two doors away from the man from Cheshire.
- The balloonist lives next door to a Cumbrian.

Answers on page 90

1. In which country is the area called the Mato Grosso?

2. What name is given to a triangle which has two equal sides?

3. What was the first name of the famous Spanish painter Picasso?

4. The eruption of which volcano destroyed Pompeii in AD 79?

5. Which international organisation is known by the initials OAU?

6. Hamilton is the capital of which island group?

7. Where would you find Maggotts, Copse, Becketts and Woodcote?

8. Which modern author has written a highly successful series of novels featuring the later life of the school bully from *Tom Brown's Schooldays*?

9. Which famous dancer died in 1927 when her scarf became tangled in the wheel of a car and strangled her?

10. What is the name of the character played by Anthony Perkins in *Psycho* and *Psycho II*?

11. *The Day of the Scorpion, The Towers of Silence, A Division of the Spoils* – what is the title needed to complete this set?

12. For what sort of book is the John W. Campbell Memorial Award given?

13. Who commanded the English fleet against the Spanish Armada in 1588?

14. Dulcet, clarabella and bombarde are part of which musical instrument?

15. Sn is the chemical symbol for what?

Answers on page 90

KRYPTIC RELATIONS

1. A man is twice as old as his wife was when he was as old as his wife is; and whilst he has exceeded three score and ten, she is not yet 60.

   How old are they both?

2. I have three sons. The product of their ages is equal to 72 and the sum of their ages is the number of my house. My eldest son is a champion swimmer.

   What are their ages?

3. At a party I met Mr Jones, Mr Smith and Mr Brown, and Sarah, Joanna and Claire. Mr Jones said he was married to Sarah. Mr Smith said he was married to Joanna. And Sarah said she was married to Mr Smith.

   I found out later that none of them had told the truth although each of the men was married to one of the women.

   Who is married to whom?

4. Pete's father's father's son is married to Jack's daughter.

   What is the relationship between Pete and Jack?

Answers on page 91

BUZZER SEQUENCE 8

Important Before answering the questions below, please read the notes on page 12.

1. About which blind hero of a Bible story did John Milton write an epic poem?
2. Which inventor with the first names Samuel Finley Breese originated the telegraphic code?
3. Which actor plays Chief Inspector Morse on TV, in dramatisations of Colin Dexter's novels?
4. Thoth, Horus and Anubis were gods of which ancient civilisation?
5. Which Egyptian President nationalised the Suez Canal in 1956?
6. NASA's Mission Control centre for space flights is in which city of Texas, at the Lyndon B. Johnson Center?
7. Which Houston-born millionaire owned airlines and produced the film *The Outlaw* before becoming a recluse?
8. To what post was Edward James Hughes, always called 'Ted', appointed in 1984?
9. In which sport at Wimbledon is the Laurels held over 460 metres and the Derby over 500 metres?
10. Gray's, Lincoln's and the Inner and Middle Temples are known collectively as what?
11. In what sort of court would you find a tin, also called a tell-tale, across the front wall?
12. Decompression sickness or 'the bends' is caused by bubbles of which gas forming in the blood?
13. The NGA is a union of which trade, as is SOGAT '82?
14. Which French daily newspaper has the same name as the central character in *The Barber of Seville*?
15. The geometrical figure called a heptagon has how many sides?
16. Which of the seven wonders of the ancient world was in Babylon?
17. Which British star played an illiterate gardener in *Being There* in 1979, shortly before he died?

Answers on page 91

IF

BECOMES

WHAT DOES

BECOME?

Answer on page 91

Important Before answering the questions below, please read the notes on page 12.

1. Which royal consort died in 1861, having organised the Great Exhibition?
2. Bernardo Bertolucci directed which film that won nine Oscars in 1988?
3. Who composed the Emperor piano concerto in 1809, and the Archduke piano trio two years later?
4. Which city was Beethoven's birthplace and is now West Germany's capital?
5. Bonneville Flats are in which US state that contains Salt Lake City?
6. What does the abbreviation UT represent to astronomers that was originally based on Greenwich?
7. Who had top ten hits in 1965 with 'The Times They Are A-Changin' and 'Subterranean Homesick Blues'?
8. What sort of creatures are bobolinks, bobwhites and boobies?
9. Which park lies between Birdcage Walk and The Mall in London, near Horseguards Parade?
10. In which sport did Steve James and Tony Drago compete in the 1988 world championship?
11. What sort of vessel could use snorkel tubes for ventilation?
12. Which river flows under the George Washington Bridge, between New York and New Jersey?
13. Rock Hudson and Susan St James co-starred in which TV series about a police chief?
14. In which sport did Frew McMillan and Betty Stove win several championships?
15. What are tensors and extensors in the human body?
16. Which political party did Benito Mussolini found in Italy around 1920?
17. Who composed 'Fascinating Rhythm', 'SWonderful', 'Porgy and Bess' and 'Rhapsody in Blue'?

Answers on page 92

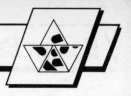

Given the information in figures A and B complete figure C.

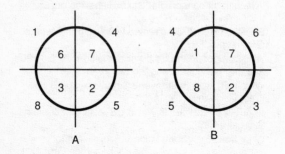

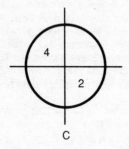

Answer on page 92

1. Which word can refer to parts of a whale's tail or to parts of an anchor?

2. In which country did the Boxer Rebellion occur?

3. Who is the father of the Earl of St Andrews?

4. Tagalog and Cebuano are languages of which country?

5. Sussex, Middlesex and Cornwall are the three counties of which island?

6. Malvasia, Nebbiolo, Palomino and Barbera are varieties of what?

7. Who wrote the novel on which the film *The Godfather* was based?

8. Who wrote the classic cookery book *French Provincial Cooking* ?

9. Which musical instrument does Marisa Robles play?

10. Which current British coin weighs exactly five grams?

11. Which organisation did John Collins help to found in 1958?

12. Which American President had a middle initial but no middle name?

13. Which Commonwealth country has a border only with Senegal?

14. Which cartoonist created Maudie Littlehampton?

15. What is the Japanese national religion?

Answers on page 92

RACING RESULTS

1. Our cyclist just beat the cyclist two behind the man just in front of the rider behind the rider behind the winner.

   What position did he finish in?

2. In the assault course, Gerry finished just ahead of the man just in front of the person who beat David.

   Where did Gail come?

3. Four contestants were asked who had won the final.
   'Gordon won,' said Steve.
   'No I didn't,' said Gordon. 'Gail was the winner.'
   'Well it certainly wasn't me,' added David.
   'Gordon's lying if he said I won,' said Gail.

   If only one person was telling the truth, who won?

4. If you were two behind the man behind the man who was three ahead of the man behind the man four behind the man behind the winner, where did you come in the race?

5. The winner and runner-up were telling a friend about the outcome of the final.
   'I won,' said John.
   'I came second,' said Susan.

   At least one of them was lying. Who came where?

6. Eric beat the person who beat the person who beat the person who came last. But he was behind the person who lost to the person three behind the winner.

   How many people were in the race?

Answers on page 92

Put the numbers from 1 to 8 in the circles so that no number is connected to another number which precedes it or follows it. For example, 3 must not be connected to 2 or 4, 4 must not be connected to 3 or 5, and so on.

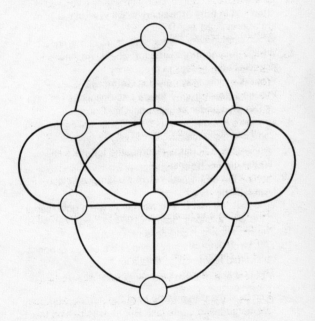

Answer on page 93

Important Before answering the questions below, read the notes on page 12.

1. Which metal has the chemical symbol Mg?
2. In which language was the Magna Carta written in 1215?
3. Which Latin words meaning 'in the year of the Lord' are abbreviated as AD?
4. Which anniversary marks forty years of marriage?
5. What's the common name for rubella, an illness especially dangerous in pregnancy?
6. What is a motorway called in Germany?
7. Whose autobiography *Inside Left* describes his time as Deputy Leader of Liverpool City Council?
8. London's Hatton Garden is the traditional centre of trade in which valuable commodity?
9. The Diamond Sculls are competed for at which regatta on the Thames?
10. Henry VIII met Francis I at which famous field in 1520 near Calais?
11. Who was the last British woman to win a gold medal in the Olympic long jump, in 1964 in Tokyo?
12. The rand is which country's unit of currency?
13. Who wrote *The African Queen* and a series of books on Horatio Hornblower, the sailor?
14. The Forest of Arden is the setting for which Shakespearian play?
15. 'Crazy for You', 'Like a Virgin' and 'Material Girl' were hits for which singer?
16. Who painted the Benois Madonna, the Virgin of the Rocks, and the Last Supper?
17. Vincente Minnelli was married to which film star whom he directed in the film *Meet Me In St Louis* ?
18. A garland of flowers called a *lei* traditionally greets travellers to which islands?

Answers on page 93

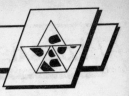

Colour the following map using at most four colours so that no two adjoining areas are coloured the same.

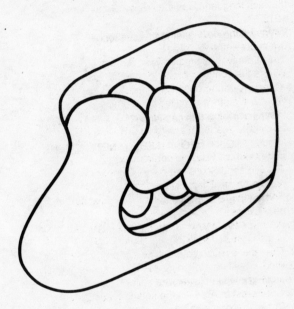

Answer on page 94

LOGICAL SEQUENCES

1. What's next in this series?

    O   U   E   H   R   A   __

2. What's the next letter in this sequence?

    K   Y   T   N   A   T   __

3. What's next in this sequence?

    NE.   NEO.   NET.   NET.   __

4. What's next in this series?

    GIV   WIV   V   EVII   GV   __

5. What's next in this series?

    17.01   13.13   10.25   8.37   __

6. Complete this sequence

   A   S   D   F   G   H   __   __   __

7. Which two numbers come next in this sequence?

   1   4   9   16   27   __   __

8. Which two letters come next in this sequence?

   A   E   F   H   I   K   L   M   __   __

9. Which two numbers come next in this sequence?

   11   18   25   16   20   __   __

10. What two numbers come next in this finite series?

    1   2   5   10   20   50   __   __

Answers on page 94

1. What is Lusitania called today?

2. In music, what does *da capo* mean?

3. Mozambique was a colony of which European country until 1975?

4. In mythology, which hero rescued Andromeda?

5. Which word means 'a morbid fear of foreigners'?

6. Near which South African city is Soweto?

7. In which city are the Bislett Games held?

8. Baron Pierre de Coubertin was responsible for the revival of what?

9. What's the cube root of 0.125?

10. In which country is the Jaffna Peninsula?

11. What is Putonghua?

12. In which city is the Sistine Chapel?

13. In which prison was Rudolf Hess held for 40 years?

14. Where did the 'Armilla Patrol' patrol?

15. Which play is set in Llareggub?

Answers on page 94

THE KRYPTON FACTOR

5 WEEK PROGRESSIVE FITNESS
TRAINING PROGRAMME

Prepared by
The Army Physical Training Corps

PHYSICAL ABILITY

Introduction

This pamphlet has been prepared by Captain Don Glynn of the Army Physical Training Corps. Its aim is to provide a progressive guide to general fitness for those people who do not enjoy any form of regular physical activity.

It explains why you should take regular exercise, the type of exercise it is important to do, and how much and how often to do it.

It has been specifically devised for *Krypton Factor* contestants to enable them to compete on a tough army assault course, which forms part of each programme.

> **WARNING** : If you are in any doubt about your fitness and you do not take regular strenuous exercise, you should seek medical advice before embarking on *The Krypton Factor* fitness training programme. Neither Granada Television nor Boxtree Limited can accept responsibility for any harm resulting from the fitness exercises in this book.

Basic Principles of Fitness Training

- Don't run before you can walk. In other words, start gradually by working well within your capabilities. Initially work until you feel physical stress but don't sustain it. Feel completely recovered before attempting the next training session. A small dose of exercise at regular intervals is better than a tremendous burst of activity followed by four to five days of painful recovery after which time any advantage is lost.
- Warm-up and mobilise the body before attempting any strenuous activity.
- Limber down after vigorous activity, that is gentle jogging and walking.
- Keep warm after training.
- Don't train until at least one hour after eating.

- Keep a weekly record of your progress. If you have not progressed it is normally an indication that you are doing too much, and that you need a reduced work rate or longer rest intervals between each training session.

Training Programme
The Training Programme is divided into three stages:

STAGE 1: Weeks 1 and 2

This is the stage when you will develop general and local powers of endurance, strength and agility. Methods of developing these qualities are:

General Endurance Development of the heart, lungs and blood vessels.
Method: Running

Local Endurance Development of strength and agility.
Method: Circuit Training

STAGE 2: Weeks 3 and 4
This is the transitional stage when the emphasis is gradually changed from endurance-type activities to power and speed-building activities.

STAGE 3: Weeks 4 and 5
This is the crucial stage of training when high quality work is demanded. By high quality we mean repetitive flat out efforts with sufficient time between each repetition for complete recovery. The time for recovery between each training session is also increased so you are sufficiently recovered to produce yet again 100 per cent effort. This is the hardest and most gruelling part of the programme.

The programme routines, recommending distances to be run in given times, number of circuit training laps, repetitions and work rates are a guide and should not be followed too strictly. Try the recommended dose and if it's too much adjust accordingly: don't get discouraged but heed the advice given opposite and progress at a rate suitable to your ability.

PHYSICAL ABILITY

Krypton Factor 5-week Fitness Training Programme

DAY 1	Run/walk 3 miles in 27–30 minutes
DAY 2	Circuit training
DAY 3	Run/walk 3 miles in 27–30 minutes
DAY 4	Circuit training
DAY 5	Run/walk 3 miles in 27–30 minutes
DAY 6	Circuit training
DAY 7	Rest
DAY 8	Run 2 miles in 16–18 minutes
DAY 9	Circuit training
DAY 10	Run 2 miles in 16–18 minutes
DAY 11	Circuit training
DAY 12	Rest
DAY 13	*Morning* Run 2 miles in 16 minutes or less
	Evening Warm ups (jog and mobility exercises) 5 minutes
	2 x 440 yards every 2 minutes
	4 x 220 yards every 1 minute
	4 x 100 yards every 30 seconds
	Warm down by gentle jogging and stretching exercises
DAY 14	Circuit training
DAY 15	AS DAY 13
DAY 16	Circuit training
DAY 17	Rest

DAY 18	*Morning* Run 2 miles in 16 minutes or less
	Evening Warm ups as before for 5 minutes
	2 x 440 yards every 2 minutes 30 seconds
	10 x 220 yards every 1 minutes 30 seconds
	10 x 100 yards every 45 seconds
	Warm down as before
DAY 19	Run 2 miles in 16 minutes or less
DAY 20	AS DAY 18
DAY 21	Run 2 miles in 16 minutes or less
DAY 22	Rest
DAY 23	*Morning* Jog 2 miles in 18–20 minutes
	Evening Warm up 5 minutes
	10 x 440 yards as follows:
	Laps 1, 3, 5, 7, and 9 sprint 220 yards, walk 220
	Laps 2, 4, 6, 8 and 10 sprint 100 yards, walk/jog 340
	Warm down
DAY 24	Circuit training
DAY 25	AS DAY 23
DAY 26	Circuit training
DAY 27	Rest
DAY 28	Run $1\frac{1}{2}$ miles in 12 minutes or less
DAY 29	Circuit training
DAY 30	Run $1\frac{1}{2}$ miles in 12 minutes or less
DAY 31	Jog for 1–2 miles, and some stretching and mobilising exercises

The programme's contestants would then have two days rest before undertaking the assault course, hopefully now fully prepared.

Circuit Training Exercises

These should be performed in the following sequence. The completion of these exercises equals one lap. The chart on page 75 will show you how many exercises and how many laps to undertake, on which days of the fitness programme.

A. STEP-UPS

Stepping on and off a chair (dining-room type with hard seat). To obtain maximum benefit from the exercise, fully extend the leading leg and perform in a vigorous manner. Both legs should share the weight-bearing burden. For example, if the left leg leads for five repetitions then the right should lead for five repetitions.

B. PRESS-UPS

From a front support position, bend arms until chest is lowered almost to the floor and return.

C. SIT-UPS

From a back lying position, with hands clasped behind head, sit up and try to touch your knees with your forehead. Return to the start position.

If this is too difficult, extend your arms straight above your head and swing them vigorously forwards at the start of the exercise. Their momentum is transferred to the trunk of your body and will help you to sit up.

70

If this is still too difficult fix your feet beneath the settee, or get a wife/husband, girlfriend/boyfriend to sit on them.

D. ASTRIDE JUMPS ON AND OFF A BENCH

Apparatus required A structure strong enough to withstand double your own body weight, 12 in high, 9-12 in wide and not less than 18 in long.

From a position astride your 'bench' jump to stand on top of the bench and immediately jump off to land in starting position. The astride jump should be performed in a rhythmical manner with no rest introduced on landing. If you can, raise the height of the bench to 15 in. This is an excellent exercise for developing 'spring' – an essential requirement of agility.

E. STRAIGHT LEG RAISE

From a back lying position, arms at side, try to keep both legs straight from hips to toes and raise them both together to the vertical position. You can make it easier by bending your legs at the knees, thus reducing the length of the lever arm.

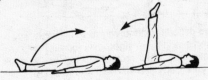

F. DIPS

Depending on the strength of the muscles used to perform this exercise and the apparatus you have available select one of the following activities.

1. From a reclining straight-backed position, with hands resting on a chair edge, bend at the elbows until your bottom touches the floor. Return to the start position.

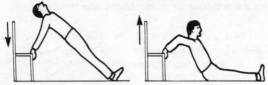

2. With arms supported between two chairs, just over body width apart, and knees bent, bend at the elbows until over a right angle and then extend straight.

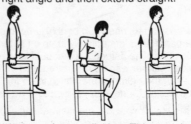

3. As for (2), but using parallel bar. This exercise, if too severe can incorporate the use of the legs, that is a jump to support (as illustrated below). This alternative gives you a fourth choice.

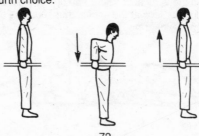

G. 'V' SITS

From a back lying position, arms extended above the head, raise legs, arms and trunk simultaneously to a 'V' position and return (1). This exercise should be done in rapid succession, and will require a degree of co-ordination. Initially it may be necessary for you to modify this movement by bending your knees, and by keeping your arms at your side, palms facing down. Press downwards onto your hands as you raise your trunk (2).

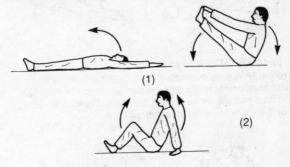

(1)

(2)

H. SQUAT THRUSTS

From a front support position (as for press-ups), jump to the crouch support position, then immediately jump back to the start position. Perform rapidly and vigorously with a full range of movement.

I. HEAVES

Lie on your back beneath a table. Hold onto the edge of the table. Bend your arms until your chest is raised to touch the underside of the table

J. LATERAL TRUNK RAISE

From a side lying position, support trunk on one arm. Extend uppermost leg approximately 9 in to the rear. Lift the hips into the air by flexing the trunk. Perform an equal number of repetitions on either side.

Days	Number of Laps	NUMBER OF REPETITIONS OF EACH EXERCISE									
		A	B	C	D	E	F	G	H	I	J
2	3	10	5	5	10	5	5	5	10	5	5
4 and 6	3	15	7	7	15	7	7	7	15	7	7
9 and 11	3	Work each exercise for 20 seconds and rest 20 seconds between each exercise									
14	3	30	10	10	30	10	10	10	30	10	10
16	3	Work each exercise for 30 seconds and rest 30 seconds between each exercise.									
24 and 26	6	Do a 5 minute warm-up. Then work each exercise for 15 seconds at fast tempo (total exercise time: 2 minutes, 30 seconds). Recover completely, then repeat for 6 laps, remembering to recover fully between each lap.									
29	3 gentle tempo	10	5	5	10	5	5	5	10	5	5

ANSWERS

ANSWERS

LOGIC PUZZLES 1

1. 3. **2.** I, E (Acronym for the United Nations International Children's Emergency Fund.) **3.** 68°C (Conversion of Centigrade to Fahrenheit.) **4.** 2, 10, 14. **5.** VIIIIIXXXVXVIII (Alphabet numbered with Roman numerals, e.g. K=XI, F=VI, etc.). **6.** WRONG. **7.** Gordon.

SPATIAL LOGIC 1

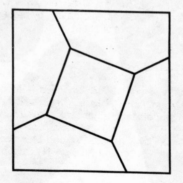

GENERAL KNOWLEDGE 1

1. Toulouse-Lautrec. **2.** J. B. Priestley. **3.** Sinai.
4. Cooper. **5.** F. Scott Fitzgerald. **6.** Walter Mondale.
7. Sulphur. **8.** Malta. **9.** Louis XVI. **10.** Kirk Douglas.
11. Crimean. **12.** Taxidermist. **13.** Fe. **14.** Collar bone.
15. Grilled lobster.

CODE-BREAKING

1. ENTER (Last letter of each number written forms the word.) **2.** HUGE (Numbers represent the letters of the alphabet numbered backwards, for example Z=1, A=26.) **3.** ANSWER (Letters numbered thus: A=1, B=3, C=6, etc.) **4.** STONES (First letter of each number written forms the word.) **5.** PARADOX (Letters numbered thus: A=2, B=4, C=6, etc.) **6.** VINE (Penultimate letter of each number written forms the word.) **7.** PRONOUN (Letters numbered thus: A=5, B=10, C=15, etc.) **8.** VICTORY (Letters are represented, alternately, by preceding and subsequent letters in alphabet.)

BUZZER SEQUENCE 1

1. Maps. **2.** Mozambique. **3.** *Amadeus*. **4.** Modigliani. **5.** Purple Heart. **6.** Butterflie. **7.** Cumbria. **8.** Lonnie Donegan. **9.** Vietnam. **10.** Vertical Take-Off and Landing. **11.** Copper. **12.** Royal Ulster Constabulary. **13.** Overcoats. **14.** Cannes. **15.** John Steinbeck. **16.** Antelopes. **17.** Lemuel Gulliver. **18.** Oesophagus.

KRYPTIC CUBES

XIV	XI
XIX	XVI

Top left number is the sum of the left column.
Top right number is the sum of the top row.
Bottom left number is the sum of the bottom row.
Bottom right number is the sum of the right column.

SPATIAL LOGIC 2

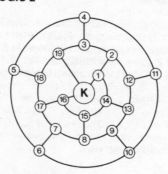

GENERAL KNOWLEDGE 2

1. Potassium. 2. Milton Keynes. 3. *H.M.S. Pinafore*.
4. Golden hamsters. 5. Russian cosmonaut Valentina
Tereshkova. 6. Oslo. 7. Ephemeral. 8. *A Tale of Two
Cities*. 9. All records by Pink Floyd. 10. The Parthenon in
Athens. 11. Elizabeth Fry. 12. Vivaldi. 13. Petrograd.
14. Lemuel Gulliver. 15. Aubergine.

THE KRYPTON KAT

BUZZER SEQUENCE 2

1. M. **2.** Morgan. **3.** Daley Thompson. **4.** *The Sun*.
5. Shi-ite. **6.** H. Rider Haggard. **7.** Old Testament or Bible
(names of books). **8.** Sir Edward Elgar. **9.** Acropolis.
10. Ghana. **11.** Jim Rockford. **12.** Quartz. **13.** Ten.
14. Shergar. **15.** Charlotte Bronte. **16.** Marathon.

SPATIAL LOGIC 3

3, 4, 7 and 8.

SPATIAL LOGIC 4

GENERAL KNOWLEDGE 3

1. Frank Whittle. **2.** Michael Holding. **3.** Halley's Comet.
4. Janus. **5.** Penguins. **6.** Cape Town. **7.** Berlin.
8. Vladimir Nabokov. **9.** Virgin Islands. **10.** Genesis.
11. Prince Michael of Kent. **12.** Alaska. **13.** David Essex.
14. Fox. **15.** El Salvador.

ODD ONE OUT

1. ARCH (In all other words, the letters are in alphabetical order.) **2.** O (All other letters are made up of straight lines.) **3.** A (The others are the first letters of colours of the spectrum.) **4.** C and Q (The others spell KRYPTON.)

SPATIAL LOGIC 5

90

SPATIAL LOGIC 6

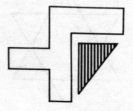

GENERAL KNOWLEDGE 4

1. Zambia. **2.** Polo. **3.** Aspirin. **4.** Ted Hughes. **5.** £500.
6. Spain. **7.** Six. **8.** Doris Lessing. **9.** Pyrrhic Victory.
10. Robert Kennedy. **11.** One rouble. **12.** Christopher Wren. **13.** Show jumping. **14.** Rossetti. **15.** July.

SPATIAL LOGIC 7

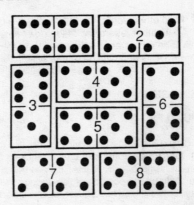

Four rows and four columns = eight in total.

MATHEMATICAL MUDDLES

1.
```
            573
215 / 123195
      1075
      1569
      1505
       645
       645
```

2. 1lb, 3lb, 9lb, 27lb are all the weights required. 3. 11.
4. 29. 5. £31.63. 6. 16. 7. *Step 1* Fill A and transfer
contents to B; *Step 2* Fill A and transfer 2 pints to B;
Step 3 Empty B back into tub; *Step 4* Pour remaining pint
in A into B; *Step 5* Fill A from tub and pour into B.
8. Less. 9. 66,430. 10. An infinite number of times. Any
number can be subtracted from any other, any number of
times: you will of course end up with negative answers.

ANSWERS

BUZZER SEQUENCE 3

1. Radius. 2. Ulna. 3. Lenin. 4. Dennis Waterman.
5. English Channel. 6. Capt. Matthew Webb. 7. *Starlight Express*. 8. English setter. 9. Liverpool.10. Frankie Goes To Hollywood. 11. Centimes. 12. Yard, or 3 ft. 13. Charlie Parker. 14. Jane Austen. 15. Texas.16. Capital Transfer Tax. 17. Santiago.

LOGIC PUZZLES 2

1. 10p and 1p (One of the coins isn't a 10p. but the other one is.) 2. XII (Seven-hour increases on a clock face using Roman numerals.) 3. SCRAPE (The number after each letter defines the position of the decoded letter.)
4. Monday. 5. KRYPTON FACTOR. 6. G = Goodie B = Baddie.

SPATIAL LOGIC 8

A =    B =

GENERAL KNOWLEDGE 5

1. Paul Newman. **2.** Ankara. **3.** Toxicology. **4.** Falkland Islands. **5.** Eddie Calvert. **6.** Karl Marx. **7.** Iran. **8.** James Hilton. **9.** Krypton. **10.** Paul Simon. **11.** Polio/Poliomyelitis. **12.** Onion. **13.** Marti Caine. **14.** King John. **15.** Prime Minister of Norway.

BUZZER SEQUENCE 4

1. Chequered flag. **2.** Spain. **3.** Philip II. **4.** Matchboxes. **5.** Three minutes. **6.** Captain Macheath. **7.** Alec Douglas-Home. **8.** The eye. **9.** Isambard Kingdom. **10.** Jordan. **11.** Dead Sea. **12.** Trevor Howard. **13.** Chancellor of the Exchequer. **14.** Wrestling. **15.** Cornwall. **16.** *King Lear.* **17.** Turkey.

SPATIAL LOGIC 9

SPATIAL LOGIC 10

GENERAL KNOWLEDGE 6

1. Leonard Bernstein. **2.** Dermatology. **3.** Lough Neagh.
4. Isle of Man. **5.** Ambrosia. **6.** Strawberry. **7.** John Keats.
8. Contour. **9.** Sacramento. **10.** *University Challenge.*
11. Margaret Drabble. **12.** Edward G. Robinson.
13. Liverpool. **14.** Sherlock Holmes. **15.** Alan Parker.

SPATIAL LOGIC 11

(The top hand of the clock remains constant. The bottom
hand moves by one division at each stage and the
colours alternate between black and white.)

NUMBER GRID

14

LOGIC GRID

	Name	Hair Colour	Occupation
Highest Score	Charles	Blonde	Doctor
Middle Score	Alfred	Brunette	Actor
Lowest Score	Bill	Redhead	Sailor

SPATIAL LOGIC 12

The clues from the first diagram were:
- Blue touches no other circle.
- Red touches one other circle.
- Green touches two other circles.
- Yellow touches three other circles.
- Orange touches four other circles.

BUZZER SEQUENCE 5

1. Greece. **2.** Melina Mercouri. **3.** *Merchant of Venice*.
4. Marco Polo. **5.** *Tom Sawyer.* **6.** National Union of
Public Employees. **7.** Leather. **8.** Forty. **9.** *Piano*.
10. Poland. **11.** Roman Polanski. **12.** Six metres.
13. Antrim. **14.** Snapdragon. **15.** King Arthur.
16. President of the USA.

LOGIC PUZZLES 3

1. 1796 1ND 1808. **2.** The match – it is the only thing that
will light by itself. **3.** None – it was Noah's Ark. **4.** 92.4
(VHF frequencies of Radios 1, 2, 3, and 4). **5.** E, M
(MENTAL AGILITY spelt backwards.) **6.** £20,000.
7. Seven (All but seven finished the course dry.)

NEIGHBOURHOOD GAME

1. No. 5; **2.** Blue; **3.** Mr Davis; **4.** Yellow.

SPATIAL LOGIC 13

D – the right eye (Sequence goes right, left, left, right,
left, left, etc.)

GENERAL KNOWLEDGE 7

1. Lead. **2.** Garry Trudeau. **3.** Libya. **4.** *Lust For Life*.
5. Shakin' Stevens. **6.** Grace Darling. **7.** Pietro Annigoni.
8. Frogs. **9.** High jump. **10.** Othello. **11.** Blenheim Palace.
12. Haiti. **13.** Rembrandt. **14.** Barcelona. **15.** Catherine
Cookson.

SPATIAL LOGIC 14

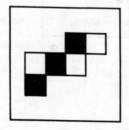

BUZZER SEQUENCE 6

1. The Wash. **2.** Mount St Helens. **3.** Paris. **4.** Ring Road.
5. Otters. **6.** Samuel Taylor Coleridge. **7.** Dog; **8.** Kate
Bush. **9.** Samurai. **10.** Surface to Air Missile.
11. Sir Thomas Sopwith. **12.** Maria Callas. **13.** Apples.
14. Radio waves. **15.** Ludovic Kennedy. **16.** Violin.
17. Australia.

LOGIC PUZZLES 4

1. PEG (All the others are phonetics for letters of the
alphabet: EYE = I, TEA = T, SEA = C, etc.) **2.** Pilot is a
woman and Cook is a man. **3.** Suffix letters used to
denote year of car registration: F = 1988 reg., G = 1989
reg. **4.** 1500 (All are recognised athletics distances: 100
metres, 200 metres, etc.) **5.** Golf. **6.** One.

SPATIAL LOGIC 15

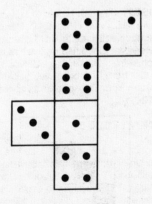

BUZZER SEQUENCE 7

1. The one-pound note. **2.** Troy weight. **3.** Geoffrey Chaucer. **4.** Lambeth. **5.** The National Theatre. **6.** Anaesthetic. **7.** Rip Van Winkle. **8.** Show-jumping. **9.** Peter Shaffer. **10.** Eros. **11.** Dutch. **12.** Flemish. **13.** Penicillin. **14.** Philadelphia. **15.** *Great Expectations*. **16.** Horatio Nelson.

SPATIAL LOGIC 16

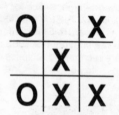

WHOSE HOUSE?

- Sid, a joiner from Kent, lives at No. 1.
- Bert, a plumber from Lincolnshire, lives at No. 2.
- Eric, a balloonist from Devon, lives at No. 3.
- Frank, a teacher from Cumbria, lives at No. 4.
- Claud, a seaman from Cheshire, lives at No. 5.

GENERAL KNOWLEDGE 8

1. Brazil. **2.** Isosceles. **3.** Pablo. **4.** Vesuvius. **5.** Organisation for African Unity. **6.** Bermuda. **7.** Silverstone. **8.** George MacDonald Fraser. **9.** Isadora Duncan. **10.** Norman Bates. **11.** *Jewel in the Crown*. **12.** Science Fiction. **13.** Admiral Charles Howard of Effingham. **14.** Organ. **15.** Tin.

ANSWERS

KRYPTIC RELATIONS

1. The husband is 72 and the wife is 54.
2. Eight, three and three. 3. Sarah and Mr Brown, Claire and Mr Smith, Joanna and Mr Jones. 4. Jack is Pete's grandfather.

BUZZER SEQUENCE 8

1. Samson Agonistes. 2. Morse. 3. John Thaw.
4. Egyptian. 5. Colonel Gamal Abdul Nasser.
6. Houston. 7. Howard Hughes. 8. Poet Laureate.
9. Greyhound racing. 10. The Inns of Court. 11. Squash.
12. Nitrogen. 13. Printing. 14. *Le Figaro*. 15. Seven.
16. Hanging Gardens. 17. Peter Sellers.

SPATIAL LOGIC 17

ANSWERS

BUZZER SEQUENCE 9

1. Prince Albert. **2.** *The Last Emperor*. **3.** Beethoven.
4. Bonn. **5.** Utah. **6.** Universal Time. **7.** Bob Dylan.
8. Birds. **9.** St James's Park. **10.** Snooker.
11. Submarine. **12.** The Hudson River. **13.** *Macmillan and Wife*. **14.** Lawn Tennis. **15.** Muscles. **16.** Fascist.
17. George Gershwin.

SPATIAL LOGIC 18

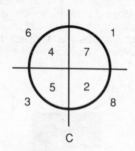

GENERAL KNOWLEDGE 9

1. Flukes. **2.** China. **3.** Duke of Kent. **4.** Philippines.
5. Jamaica. **6.** Grape. **7.** Mario Puzo. **8.** Elizabeth David.
9. Harp. **10.** 20p piece. **11.** CND. **12.** Harry S. Truman.
13. The Gambia. **14.** Osbert Lancaster. **15.** Shinto.

RACING RESULTS

1. Third. **2.** Third. **3.** David. **4.** Seventh. **5.** Susan won.
John came second. (If one was lying, they must both
have lied.) **6.** Nine.

SPATIAL LOGIC 19

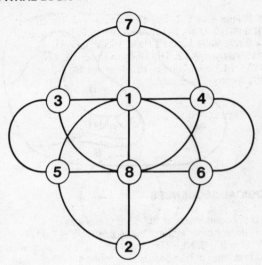

BUZZER SEQUENCE 10

1. Magnesium. **2.** Latin. **3.** Anno Domini. **4.** Ruby.
5. German measles. **6.** Autobahn. **7.** Derek Hatton.
8. Diamonds and other jewels. **9.** Henley. **10.** Field of the
Cloth of Gold. **11.** Mary Rand. **12.** South Africa.
13. C. S. Forester. **14.** *As You Like It.* **15.** Madonna.
16. Leonardo da Vinci. **17.** Judy Garland. **18.** Hawaii.

SPATIAL LOGIC 20

R = Red
B = Blue
Y = Yellow
G = Green

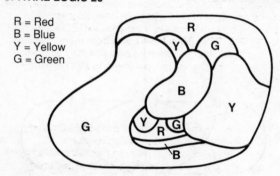

LOGICAL SEQUENCES

1. U (Second letters of the days of the week.)
2. R (Every other letter of the words K r Y p T o N f A c T o R .) **3.** NEF (The third letter of each sequence is the first letter of numbers one to four.) **4.** GVI (Subsequent monarchs begining with George the Fourth.)
5. 7.49. **6.** J, K, L (The second line of the QWERTY keyboard. **7.** 40, 57 (Subsequent prime numbers are added to each number.) **8.** N, T (All straight line letters of the alphabet.) **9.** 15, 14 (Numerical values of letters spelling KRYPTON.) **10.** 100, 200 (British decimal coinage.)

GENERAL KNOWLEDGE 10

1. Portugal. **2.** Go back to the begining. **3.** Portugal.
4. Perseus. **5.** Xenophobia. **6.** Johannesburg. **7.** Oslo.
8. The Olympic Games. **9.** 0.5 or half. **10.** Sri Lanka.
11. Chinese official standard dialect. **12.** Rome or Vatican. **13.** Spandau. **14.** Persian Gulf, or The Gulf.
15. *Under Milk Wood* .

PROGRAMME WINNERS

Since 1977, over 85,000 people have applied to compete on the programme, and 432 have been successful.
Only 12 people have earned the title UNITED KINGDOM SUPERPERSON. They have come from many walks of life, but have emerged winners because they all have proved keenly determined, persevering and resilient – in short, all-rounders.

These are the champions:

1977   Harry Evans (Carpenter/Building Estimator).
1978   Ken Wilmhurst (Company Director).
1979   Peter Richardson (Retired Production Manager).
1980   Philip Bradley (University Medical Lecturer).
1981   John McAllister (Lecturer).
1982   John Webley (Dental Surgeon).
1983   Chris Topham (RAF Flying Instructor).
1984   Paul Smith (Civil Servant).
1985   Dr Andrew Gillam (Oceanographer).
1986   David Kemp (Marketing Director).
1987   Marian Chanter (Baker).
1988   David Lee (Law Student).

Other titles in this series:

Supersoaps Quiz Book No. 1
Chris Stacey
ISBN: 1 85283 028 X

15-to-1 General Knowledge Quiz Book
John Lewis
ISBN: 1 85283 242 8

TV's Greatest Hits Quiz Book
Anthony Davis
ISBN: 1 85283 261 4